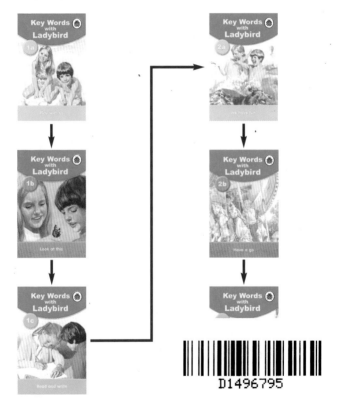

50p

Readers will get the most out of the **Key Words** reading scheme when they follow the books in the pattern 1a, 1b, 1c: 2a, 2b, 2c: and so on.

D1496795

The a, b, and c series are all written using the same carefully controlled vocabulary.

The Ladybird Key Words Reading Scheme
has three series, each containing
twelve books.

The 'a' series gradually introduces and
repeats new words.

The parallel 'b' series provides further
practice of these words, but in a different
context and with different illustrations.

The 'c' series uses familiar words to teach
phonics in a methodical way, enabling
children to read more difficult words.
It also provides a link to writing.

All three series are written using the same
carefully controlled vocabulary.

Published by Ladybird Books Ltd
A Penguin Company
Penguin Books Ltd., 80 Strand, London WC2R 0RL, UK
Penguin Books Australia Ltd., Camberwell, Victoria, Australia
Penguin Books (NZ) Ltd., Private Bag 102902, NSMC, Auckland, New Zealand

15 17 19 20 18 16 14

ISBN-13: 978-1-8442-2363-3
ISBN-10: 1-8442-2363-9

Printed in China

Key Words
Reading Scheme

2a
We have fun

written by W. Murray
illustrated by J.H. Wingfield

Here is Peter
and here is Jane.

Here is Pat, the dog.

new word

Pat

Peter is here.

Jane is here
and Pat is here.

Here they are.

---

new words

they   are

Here they are
in the water.

They like the water.

Pat likes the water.

Pat likes fun.

---

new words

water   fun

Come in, Pat.

It is fun.

It is fun in the water.

Come in the water.

Come, come, come.

---

new words

come It it

Pat comes in.

Pat likes the water.

It is fun in the water,
says Peter.

---

new word

says

I have a ball, says Peter.

Here is the ball.

Here is the ball, Pat,
he says.

new words   have he

Look, look, says Jane.

Look, Peter, look.

Have a look.

Come and look.

Peter has a look.

new word

Look   look

Peter looks.

A fish, says Jane.

It is a fish, says Peter.

It is a fish, he says.

---

new word

fish

Look, says Peter.

The dog wants the fish.

He wants the fish, Jane.

---

new word

wants

Pat wants the fish.

No, no, no, says Jane,
you come here.

Come here, Pat, come here

No, no, no.

---

new words

No   no   you

Here are Peter and Jane.

Peter has some water.

Here you are, Jane,
he says.

---

new word

some

Here you are, Jane,
says Peter.

Here you are.

This is for you.

Here is some water
for you.

new words

for   This   this

This is for you, Jane says

Here is some water
for you.

Here you are, Peter.

It is for you.

no new words

Look Jane, I can jump, says Peter.

I can jump in the water.

Can you jump like this, Jane?

new words

can   jump

Jane can jump
and Peter can jump.

They jump into the water
for fun.

We like this, they say.

new words

into   We   we

Jump this, Pat, jump this says Peter.

Jump in the water.

You can jump.

Pat jumps into the water

Pat jumps.

He jumps into the water.

He likes to jump.

It is fun, says Jane,
we like this.

---

new word

to

We have to go, says Peter.

Come, Jane.
Come, he says.
We have to go.

---

new word

go

We have to go, Pat,
says Jane.
Come, Pat, come.

Yes, says Peter,
we have to go.

---

new word

Yes   yes

Can we have some sweets,
says Jane.

Can we go to the shop
for some sweets ?

Yes, says Peter.

---

new word

sweets

This is the shop, Jane.

Yes, this is it.

They have sweets and toy

We want sweets, says Jan

Peter and Jane go into the sweet shop.

Pat is in the shop.

Jane and Peter have some sweets.

Pat has a sweet.

no new words

I want to go home,
says Jane.

Yes, I want to go home,
says Peter.

Come, Pat, come.

We want to go home.

---

new word

home

Here we are, says Jane.
We are home.
It is fun in the water.

Yes, says Peter,
we have fun in the water.

no new words

New words used in this book

Total number of new words: 27
Average repetition per word: 10